THE BEANO books
geddes & grosset

MDM. TOSSAUD'S
WAXWORKS
FAMOUS
COMIC CHARACTERS.
YOUR DUMMY'S A BIGGER SOFTY THAN YOU, WALTER.
MELT!
GLOP!
DENNIS! THAT'S JOLLY NAUGHTY.
WALTER
FREDDIE

THINK I'LL REST MY WEARY WINGS ON A TELEPHONE LINE.
GET LOST - THIS LINE'S ENGAGED!
SMACK!
SQUAWK!

ONE OF THE JOYS OF JUNGLE LIFE IS A COOLING DIP IN THE WATER HOLE.
OOYAH!
BUT YOU MUST GET THERE BEFORE A THIRSTY ELEPHANT!
HIC!

WOW! A WAR DANCE. THEY MUST BE PLANNING UM UPRISING.
OO-WOO-WOO-WOO-
NO! NO! SQUAW WALKING DISASTER'S COYOTE CURRY UM TOO HOT!

MAKE SURE THE AUDIENCE LAUGHS AT MY JOKES AT THE CAMP CONCERT TONIGHT.
LAUGH NOW!
WHAT'S DARK, TALKS WITH A SCOTS ACCENT AND GOES 'TICK-TOCK'? -THE BLACK WATCH!
OOPS!
CLUNK!
HA! HA!
HO! HO!
HA-HA!

CAR FOR SALE
ONE CAREFUL DRIVER
CAR FOR SALE
ONE CAREFUL DRIVER
AND TWO HOPELESS DRIVERS
What kind of car does a Norwegian drive?
A fjord.

SIGH! I HAVEN'T SEEN ANOTHER PERSON FOR YEARS AN' YEARS AN' AGES.
IDEA!
PRIVATE BEACH
NO SUNBATHING
NO SWIMMING
NO BALL GAMES
NO ANYTHING
HEH! I KNEW THAT WOULD WORK.

NEARLY THERE AT LAST.

OH, NO! THIS IS THE ONLY PUBLIC IG-LOO FOR MILES.
ENGAGED

HERE IS A NEWSFLASH!
A.B.C.T.V.
WHOOSH!
B.C.T.V.
A PRISONER APPEARED IN COURT TODAY CHARGED WITH WRITING ALL OVER HIS CELL WALLS. HE WAS FINED FIFTY POUNDS AND SENT BACK TO FINISH HIS SENTENCE.

What do you call a building with a lot of storeys?
A library.
GASP! IT MUST BE THE WET WEATHER. I'VE NEVER TAKEN SO LONG TO CLIMB A STAIR IN MY LIFE!
OLD MILL RESTAURANT

WHY ARE YOU RUNNING SO FAST, CHIPS?
I'M TRYING TO PREVENT TWO BOYS FROM FIGHTING!
WHICH TWO BOYS?
ME AND HIM!

HANK'S STORE.
I'VE A COMPLAINT TO MAKE! THIS HONEY WE PINCHED IS FULL OF HAIRS?
HONEY
WHAT DID YOU EXPECT? IT'S STRAIGHT FROM THE COMB!
BOOM! BOOM!

What is a bird after he is four days old?
Five days old.
What do you get when you cross a carrier pigeon with a woodpecker?
A bird who knocks before he delivers his message.
What do ducks do on television?
Duckumentaries.

How did Noah see all the animals in the Ark?
By floodlight.
What do you get if you cross the Atlantic with the Titanic?
Halfway!
Which animals didn't go into the Ark in pairs?
The worms. They went in apples.

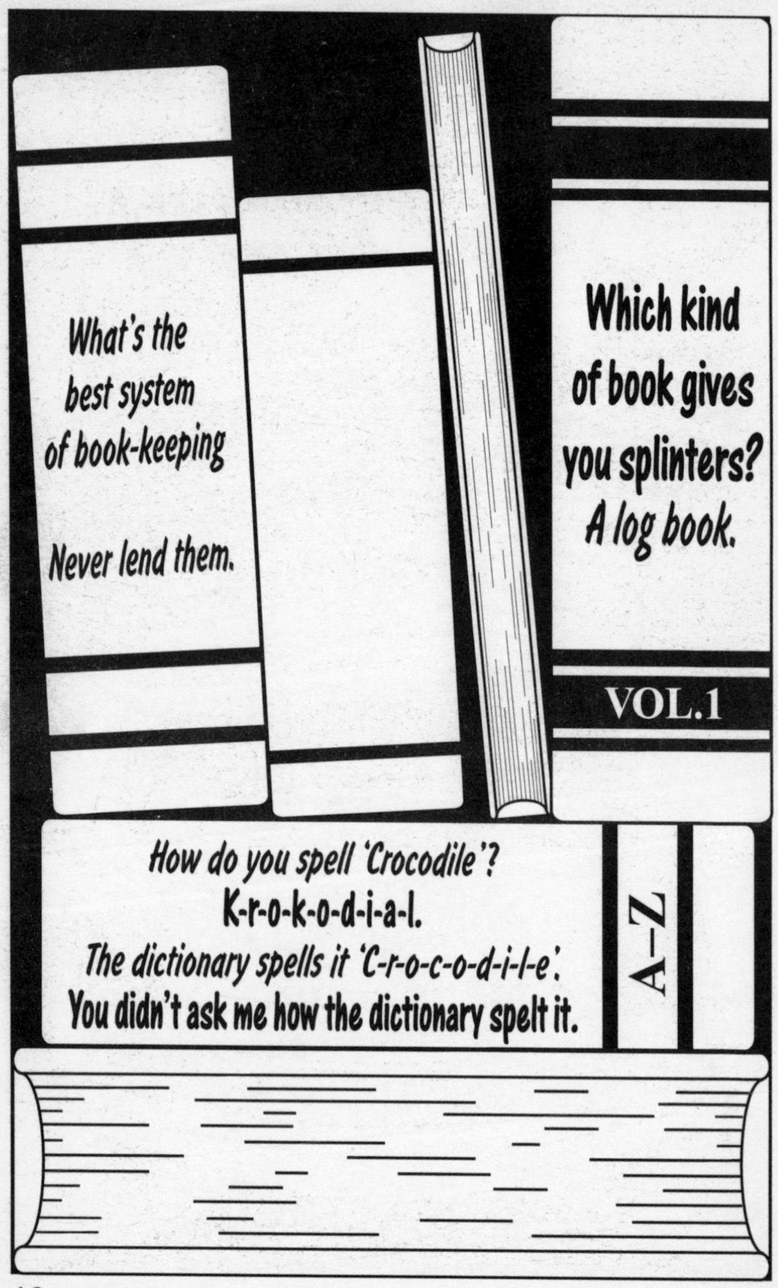
What's the best system of book-keeping
Never lend them.
Which kind of book gives you splinters?
A log book.
VOL.1
How do you spell 'Crocodile'?
K-r-o-k-o-d-i-a-l.
The dictionary spells it 'C-r-o-c-o-d-i-l-e'.
You didn't ask me how the dictionary spelt it.
A–Z

Why did the taxi driver give up his job?
Because people kept talking behind his back.
What's the best thing to take when you are run down?
The car's number.

Why did the golfer carry two pairs of shoes?
In case he got a hole in one!
You've been working in your garden for hours. What are you growing?
Tired.
What do you call a sleepy Stegosaurus?
A Stegosnaurus.

Doctor, doctor, I keep thinking I'm a snooker ball.
How absurd. Please go to the back of the cue!
Doctor, doctor, I keep thinking I'm invisible.
Next please!
Doctor! Doctor! My hair's falling out. I need something to keep it in!
Here's a carrier bag!

What happened to
the flea circus?
A dog came along
and stole the show.
What do mice
do during the day?
Mousework.
How do you tell
one cat from another?
Look them up in
a catalogue.

Knock, knock!
Who's there?
Felix.
Felix who?
Felix my lolly I'll whack him.

Knock, knock!
Who's there?
Luke.
Luke who?
Luke through the keyhole and you'll see me.

Knock, knock!
Who's there?
Cows go.
Cows go who?
No — cows go moo.

I can lift an elephant with one hand.
I don't believe you.
Get me an elephant with one hand and I'll show you.
How can you run over an elephant?
Climb up its tail, dash to its head, and slide down its trunk.
What is big and grey and has sixteen wheels?
An elephant on roller skates.
Where do you find Italian elephants?
Tuskany.

Our games teacher once tried to swim across the English channel!
Did he do it?
No — he got halfway across and had to turn back because he was so tired!
What's made of chocolate and lies on the sea bed?
An oyster egg.
What did one fish say to the other?
If you keep your mouth shut, you won't get caught.

What's bread? Raw toast!
What's short, green and goes camping?
A boy sprout.
What are yellow and make a lot of noise?
Custard screams.

Why can't a car play football?
Because it's only got one boot.
How do you keep cool at a football match?
Stay by a fan.
When are mountain goats at their best?
When they're at their peak.
Which kind of bear smell smells the worst?
Camem-bear.

MEBA, MIA, MYEU
WOOF!
WOOF!
MIAOW!
AAH! SO THAT'S HOW IT'S SPELT!

ZONK!
OOYAH!
GROAN! I HATE FLYING IN FOG!

OH, GOODY! NEW WALLPAPER WITH NICE HORSIES ON IT!

HMPH! BE LIKE THAT, SEE IF I CARE!

ME'S GOT MY VERY OWN REAL ROCKIN' HORSIE.

LIBRARY
SILENCE
SILENCE
SILENCE
SILENCE
SILENCE
YOU'RE NICKED, LADS.
WE'RE THROWING THE BOOK AT YOU.
SILENCE
OKAY, WE'LL COME QUIETLY!

HERE IS A NEWSFLASH!
A.B.C.T.V.
WHOOSH!
B.C.T.V.
A ROGUE ELEPHANT HAS BROKEN OUT OF CACTUSVILLE ZOO AND IS TERRORISING THE TOWN. POLICE HAVE SET UP A SPECIAL TUSK FORCE TO DEAL WITH THE PROBLEM.

DRAT! I'VE LOST AGAIN. I DON'T UNDERSTAND IT.

I THINK THERE ARE TOO MANY CHEETAHS, TARZAN.

BLAM!
BLAM!
I THINK YOU'RE WASTING YOUR BULLETS, HAM.

THAT'S HOW YOU SHOOT THE RAPIDS.
OO-ER!

WHERE HAVE YOU BEEN?
SORRY I'M LATE, BUT I SAW THIS "GO SLOW" SIGN AND YOU TOLD US ALWAYS TO OBEY ROAD SIGNS.

AND WHAT IS YOUR NEW BABY BROTHER'S NAME?
DUNNO! HE CAN'T TALK YET, SO HE HASN'T TOLD US!

I'M MAN'S BEST FRIEND AND YOU'RE NOT. SO THERE.
RASP!
SNIFF! HE'S RIGHT AND IT'S NOT FAIR.
BOOT!
UGH! PARK-KEEPERS DON'T COUNT THOUGH.
NO DOGS
HEH! WHAT A WONDERFUL MAN!

NOW PUT IT IN YOUR BANKIES, BOYS.
HO-HO! NO CHANCE OF US GETTING OUR BANKIES MIXED UP.

What kind of hens lay electric eggs?
Battery hens.

What do you get if you cross a parrot with a homing pigeon?
A bird that can ask the way if it's lost.

Knock, knock.
Who's there?
Owl.
Owl who?
Owl you find the treasure without the treasure map?

Doctor! Doctor! I keep thinking I'm covered in gold paint.

Don't worry, that's just a gilt complex.

Doctor, doctor! I think I've got measles!

That's a rash thing to say.

Doctor, Doctor, I feel like a pack of cards?

Sit down and I'll deal with you later.

What has more lives than a cat?
A frog because it croaks every night.
How do you stop your dog barking in the back garden?
Put it in the front garden.
My cat won first prize at the bird show.
Your cat? How did he do that?
He ate the prize canary.

Knock, knock!
Who's there?
Abbey.
Abbey who?
Abbey birthday to you . . .
Knock, knock.
Who's there?
Adolf.
Adolf who?
Adolf ball hit me in de mouf and I can't talk properly!

Why did the water smell?
It was in a duck ponged.
Is this a good river for fish?
Must be — I can't persuade any of them to leave it . . .
What do mermaids eat for breakfast?
Mermalade.

How do you get a peanut out of your ear?
Pour some chocolate in then it will come out a treat!

Waiter this coffee is terrible — it tastes like earth.
Yes, Sir, it was ground yesterday!

What do you call a girl with a frog on her forehead?
Lily.
How do frogs cross the road?
They use the Green Cross Toad.

Why are ghosts so bad at lying?
You can see right through them!
What do you call a monster with red spots?
A monster with measles.

What is Dracula's favourite coffee?
De-coffin-ated.
What happened at the vampire race?
They finished neck and neck.
Heard about Dracula's new boat?
It's a blood vessel.

In a fight between a fox
and a hedgehog, who won?
The hedgehog won
on points.
What do you get if you cross
a tortoise with a train carriage?
A slowcoach.
What do
you call
a mad
sheep?
Baa-my.

What motorbike does a hyena ride?
A Yama-ha-ha.

How can you hire a horse?
Make it wear stilts.

Dad! There's a kangaroo at the door.
Tell him to hop it!

What's the best way to
avoid catching diseases
from biting insects?
Don't bite any insects.
What happened
when the
glow-worm got
tramped on?
He was
de-lighted.
BEANO

GRRR!
COME ON, PUT EM UP, PUT EM UP!
TAKE THAT!
MISSED!
SOCK!
I'M THE NEW FLYWEIGHT CHAMPION OF THE WORLD, FOLKS!

HOW TO ATTRACT BIRDS TO YOUR BIRD TABLE BY JACK DAW
HMM! AND HMM AGAIN.

MINNIE'S BIRDIE DINER
YES, IT PAYS TO ADVERTISE.
CHEEP PRICES

KEEP BACK! EVERYBODY BACK!
SAND
SAND
SAND

RUN FOR IT, MAN, THESE GRENADES COULD GO OFF AT ANY MOMENT!
GREENGRO
PINEAPPLES ONE FOR THE PRICE OF TWO
SAND
SAND
Pineapples
Pineapples
YAWN! ALL MY STOCK WILL GO OFF AT THIS RATE!

MUMSIE WAS RIGHT. AN APPLE A DAY DOES KEEP THE DOCTOR AWAY.
OOYAH!
BOP!
DOC. YARD

HEY, KORKY! WHAT DO YOU GET IF YOU CROSS A SALMON WITH A SABRE?
A SWORDFISH! HO-HO!
YE-OW!
A LITTLE LATER–
HEY, GAMEY! WHAT DO YOU GET IF YOU CROSS A HAIRDRESSER AND A SNOOKER STICK?
A BARBECUE! HA-HA!

COUGH...OH, FOR THE WINGS, FOR THE WINGS...
HACK! CHOKE!
IT'S NOT EASY SINGING IN A DUST BATH.

I EEZ TAKING ZE BREAK FROM ZE ROBBERIES TODAY.
ZE OH-OH!
CREAK!
GASP! EVEN ON ZE DAY OFF I END UP HOLDING UP ZE STAGE!

YOU'RE COSTING THE AIR FORCE A *FORTUNE*, PIGGLES.
SORRY, SIR.

BUT A PILOT HAS TO *TAXI* ALONG THE RUNWAY, SIR.
THAT'LL BE TWO QUID GUV.
TAXI

I'VE BEEN OFFERED A JOB AS A MALE MODEL.
G. NOBLE MODELLING AGENCY
WANTED SAM FOX LOOKALIKES
POSE + ENTER
SOUNDS OF DINNER TRYING TO ESCAPE.
I DON'T BELIEVE IT.
BAH! IT WAS A MAIL MODEL THEY WANTED.
HUMILIATED
VISIT BUNKERTON CASTLE

WHAT A MESS!
WELL MUMSIE SAID WE WERE SUPPOSED TO LEAVE A TIP!
CHORTLE!

BOUTIQUE
THANKS FOR BUYING ME TRENDY SKI PANTS, MUM.
THAT'S OKAY, MO.

THEY'VE NO POCKETS IN THEM, HAVE THEY?
ER, NO!
IN THAT CASE YOU WON'T NEED **POCKET MONEY** ANYMORE, WILL YOU?

AH! HAM! DID YOU GET MY SHOES SOLED, LIKE I ASKED YOU?
NEWS

YEAH. SURE DID! I GOT FIFTY PENCE FOR THEM!
FLIP!
NEWS

Why did the bird sleep under the car?
To catch the oily worm.
Where do swallows do their shopping?
In a swoopermarket.
What did the cuckoo say after it fell out of the tree?
Cuckooya!

Doctor!
Doctor!
People think I'm
just a joke.
Don't make
me laugh.
Doctor! Doctor!
I feel like an apple.
Come over here.
I won't bite you.
Doctor! Doctor!
I think I'm a
telephone!
Take these pills.
If they don't help,
give me a ring.

When is it
bad luck
to have a black
cat follow you?
When you are
a mouse.
Can a mouse jump
higher than an oak tree?
Yes, oak trees
can't jump.
When is a brown
dog not a brown dog?
When it's a greyhound.

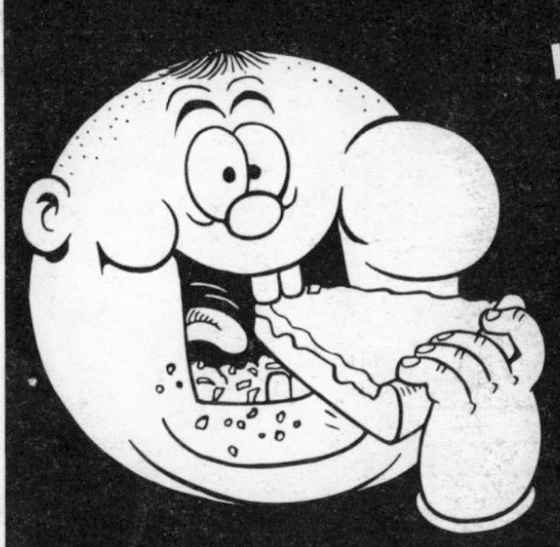

How can you tell the difference between a can of tomato soup and a can of chicken soup?

Read the label.

What can't you do if you put a five-tonne jelly in the fridge?

Close the door.

A pair of kippers, please.

I'm sorry, but we don't have a pair left.

That's OK, just give me two odd ones — my mum will never know the difference.

How do monsters have their eggs?
Terrifried.
What does the sign outside the haunted hive say?
Bee-ware.
Why is it difficult to sleep in a graveyard?
Because of all the coffin.

How do vampires keep fit?
They play a lot of batminton.
What do you get if you cross an angry monster with a pet bird?
A budgie-grrr!
Where would a vampire criminal be locked up?
In a blood cell.
JOKE BOOK

What do you get if you cross a monkey with an ocean?
Chimpansea!
How did the monkey escape from the shipwreck?
On a giraft.

Did you hear about the stupid tap dancer?
He fell into the sink.
What do you call a man who fills himself with fried slices of potatoes and makes a noise in the cinema?
Chris Packet!
What do you call a man and a woman who show you up in front of your friends?
Mum and Dad!

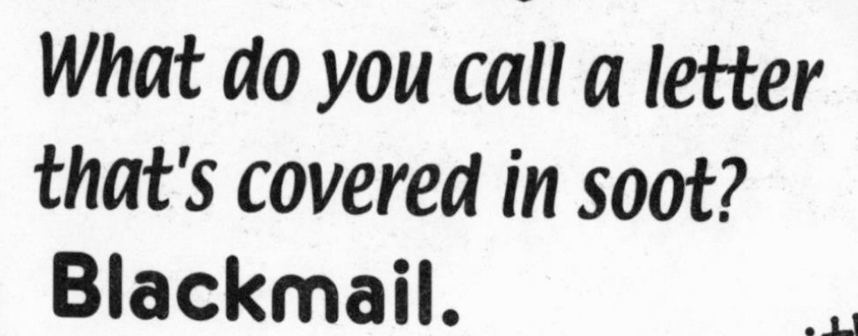

What do you call a man with a paper bag on his head?
Russell.

What do you call a boy called Lee who has no friends?
Lone Lee.

Smiffy
Why did Smiffy's dad bury his car?
Because someone told him the battery was dead.
How do you keep Smiffy occupied for hours?
Give him a piece of paper with P.T.O. on both sides.

What do you call two pigs that live together?
Pen pals!
What is a pig's favourite ballet?
Swine Lake.

Why are snakes hard to fool?
They've no leg to pull.
Baby snake: Are we poisonous?
Mother snake: Why?
Baby snake: Because I just bit my lip.
Why did the snake go to the car shop?
He vanted new vindscreen vipers!

NOPE! ALL THESE CORNERS ON THE WHEELS JUST DON'T LOOK RIGHT!
AHA!
OOH! THAT'S BETTER.
AAH!
BUMPITTY-BUMP!
BUMPITTY-BUMP!

COO! A VALUABLE GOLD COIN!
EH? GIMME IT THEN!

ONLY IF YOU CAN GUESS WHAT HAND IT'S IN!

HEH! PUTTING WARPAINT ON CHIEF WOBBLY GUT IS A BIG JOB!
RED

I KNOW I SAID YOU COULD KEEP GOLDFISH, CLOTT . . .
. . . BUT NOT IN THAT TANK!

CAN ME TAKE MY TOY DUCKIE IN BAFF TOO, MUMSIE?
OF COURSE, CUDDLES.
CHORTLE! PITY THERE'S NO ROOM FOR ME NOW.

HEH! I'M THE ONLY BABY-SITTER IN TOWN WHO CAN HANDLE THESE TWO!
CRACK!
SNARL!
GRR!
Did you hear about the man who ate a sofa and two chairs?
He had a suite tooth.

I'VE PUT A CAT FLAP IN THE DOOR, JUST AS YOU WANTED, MOGGY.
THANKS, MUTT.
IT'S THE VERY LATEST REVOLVING CAT FLAP!
SPLAT!
WOOFYAH!

COO! HE'S MOVING FAST.
YOU'D MOVE FAST IF YOUR TAIL WAS ON FIRE.
What do you get if you cross an egg with a barrel of gunpowder?
A *boom-meringue.*

CAN YOU TELL ME WHICH CABIN THIS BATH PLUG COMES FROM, CAPTAIN?

THERE ARE NO BATHS ON THIS BOAT, YOU CLOWN.

I've just eaten Madras curry and
Bombay Duck.
How do you feel?
I've got Indiagestion!

BY JINGO! THIS IS THE NOISIEST ESCALATOR I'VE EVER BEEN ON!

RUMBLE!

LEFT A BIT, LADS - I STILL CAN'T SEE. RIGHT....HOLD IT. THAT'S PERFECT.
COO-EE! MUM. YES I THOUGHT IT WAS YOU UP THERE. I CAN SEE YOU CLEARLY NOW!
FUME!

WHEE! I LOVE THESE HUMP-BACKED BRIDGES!

What do you call a foreign body in a chip pan?
An Unidentified Frying Object.

Fish and chips twice, please.
OK, OK, I heard you the first time.

My chips taste funny.
That's because you're eating them out of a comic.

What's a young witch's favourite subject?
Spelling.
Why do skeletons stay home every night?
Because they have no body to go out with.

I've got a new job as a lift operator.
How is it?
Oh, it has its ups and downs.
I want to talk to your mother about your homework.
She ain't home.
Where's your grammar?
She ain't home neither.
Cinema Attendant — "That's the sixth ticket you've bought."
Customer — "Yes, I know, there's a girl in there that keeps tearing them up."

Dad, I don't need a bike for Christmas any more.
Why not?
I found one behind the wardrobe.
If we breathe oxygen in the daytime, what do we breathe at night?
Nitrogen?
What do you call a man wearing five balaclavas and a crash helmet?
Anything you like — he can't hear a thing.
What do you call a woman who doesn't like butter?
Marge.

Smiffy
You're an hour late,Smiffy! Where have you been?
Sorry, sir. A sign on the escalator said 'Dogs must be carried' and it took me ages to find one!
Smiffy, I think you've got your wellies on the wrong feet.
But these are the only feet I've got, miss!
How were your exam questions, Smiffy?
The questions were easy, but I had trouble with the answers.

Tea-time at the policemen's house–
Mum – "Okay, who wants chips?"
Kids — "Me-ma! Me-ma! Me-ma! Me-ma!"
What's the difference between a burglar and a man wearing a wig?
One has false keys and the other has false locks.
What did the policeman say to his tummy?
You're under a vest.
My cousin has gold and silver medals in karate, cricket, snooker, horse riding, high jump, swimming and javelin!
Wow, he must be a super athlete!
No, he's a burglar actually!

Which Scottish king
kept falling over?
Robert the BRUISE.
When is a pie like a poet?
When it is Browning.
How does
Jack Frost
get to work?
By icicle.

What sort of illness does everyone on the Starship Enterprise catch?
Chicken Spocks.
When does an astronaut have his midday meal?
At launch time.

BEANObooks Competition

Roger is a Dodger, Minnie is a Minx, but Dennis is a ....!

Complete the sentence and put your answer in the box below and you could win a great BEANObooks prize in the monthly **BEANObooks prize draw!**
A winning name will be drawn from the postbag and published in The Beano comic in the first issue of every month.

A BEANObooks prize will also be awarded to the best joke sent in every month. A prizewinning joke will be picked from the postbag every month and printed in The Beano comic.

Send your entry to:
BEANObooks Competition, P.O. Box 305, London, NW1 1TX.

BEANObooks Competition

First Name..............................	Answer..
Surname................................	My Favourite Joke..........................
Address................................	....
....	....
....	....
Postcode................................	....

The Editor's decision is final and no correspondence will be entered into.